How Was it For You?

PETER VAN STRAATEN

FOURTH ESTATE · *London*

First published by De Harmonie

First published in Great Britain in 1991 by
Fourth Estate Limited
289 Westbourne Grove
London W11 2QA

Reprinted 1993

Copyright © 1991 by Peter van Straaten
Translation by Jan Michael and Paul Clark

The right of Peter van Straaten to be identified as the author of this
work has been asserted by him in accordance with the Copyright,
Designs and Patents Act 1988.

A catalogue record for this book is available from the British Library

ISBN 1-872180-49-3

All rights reserved. No part of this publication may be reproduced,
transmitted, or stored in a retrieval system, in any form or by any
means, without permission in writing from Fourth Estate Limited.

Printed and bound in Great Britain by
Biddles Ltd, Guildford and King's Lynn

"BUT WHAT ARE WE GOING TO **DO**
WHEN WE GET TO YOUR PLACE?"

"OK, BOYS. WHO'S GOT THE BIGGEST?"

"OH ALL RIGHT...ONLY FOR HEAVEN'S SAKE DON'T EXPECT TOO MUCH."

"SHALL WE GO TO ANOTHER BAR?
OR HAVE YOU DRUNK ENOUGH
NOW TO WANT TO COME TO
BED WITH ME?"

" BETTER NOT, DEAR BOY.
I'M A FRIGHTFUL PEST IN BED."

"YUK, PETER ... THAT'S DISGUSTING"

"NO, NOT EVEN WITH JOKEY CONDOMS, PHIL."

"ONCE YOU GET GOING, THINK OF
SOMETHING ELSE, LIKE BREAD
AND JAM...A TELEPHONE DIRECTORY...
...A PILE OF BRICKS..."

"NO SEX IS EVEN SAFER, CHRISTOPHER."

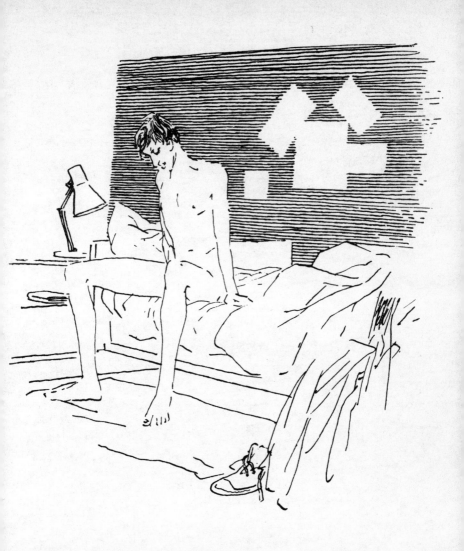

"AND WHAT ARE **YOU** GOING TO DO WHEN YOU GROW UP?"

"I KNOW I SHOULDN'T LAUGH,
BUT THEY'RE SUCH FUNNY
LITTLE THINGS."

"YOU MIGHT AT LEAST HAVE WASHED UNDER YOUR ARMS"

"OK ... DO YOUR BEST."

"THAT'S SUCH A HASSLE.... LET'S JUST HAVE A QUICKIE."

"YES, I DO LIKE IT, BUT I CAN'T SEE YOUR FACE."

"ARE YOU MOTIVATED?"

"JOHN, WHAT ON EARTH ARE YOU DOING DOWN THERE?"

"OH NO, LOVE ... DON'T BOTHER. THAT'LL TAKE **HOURS**"

"OH GOOD....
HE'S COMING ROUND AGAIN"

"SLOW DOWN! HAVE YOU GOT
A TRAIN TO CATCH OR SOMETHING?"

"HEY, YOU WOULDN'T DO THAT AT HOME, WOULD YOU?"

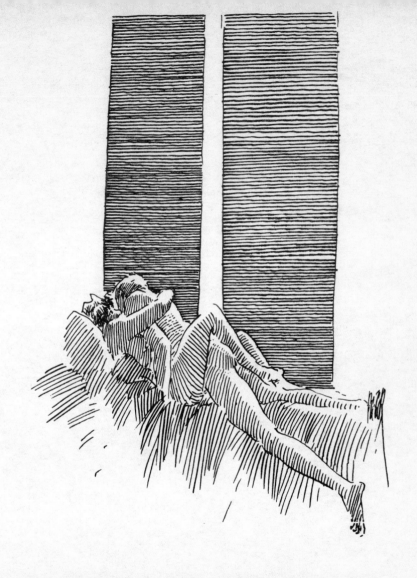

"DON'T BELCH IN MY FACE, DARLING"

"YOU COULD AT LEAST **LOOK** AT ME WHEN YOU'RE COMING"

"WHAT ARE YOU THINKING ABOUT?"

" FORGET ABOUT ME.
YOU ENJOY JOURSELF. "

"GOOD GRIEF, DAVID, YOU STILL
HAVEN'T A CLUE, HAVE YOU?"

"DON'T PANT, DARLING.
IT'S VERY OFF-PUTTING"

DON'T WAIT. PACKING.
I'S VERY OFF PUTTING.

"FOR GOD'S SAKE, COME!"

"RIGHT! NOW WHERE WERE WE?"

"DO GET A MOVE ON YOU'LL BE LATE FOR THE OFFICE."

"HARRY? HAVE YOU GONE TO SLEEP?"

"DON'T LET IT BOTHER YOU.
YOU'RE A PERFECTLY
NORMAL ENGLISHMAN."

"MAYBE ONE OF US SHOULD
TAKE LESSONS, RICHARD"

"NO...LET'S JUST SAY YOU AMUSED ME."

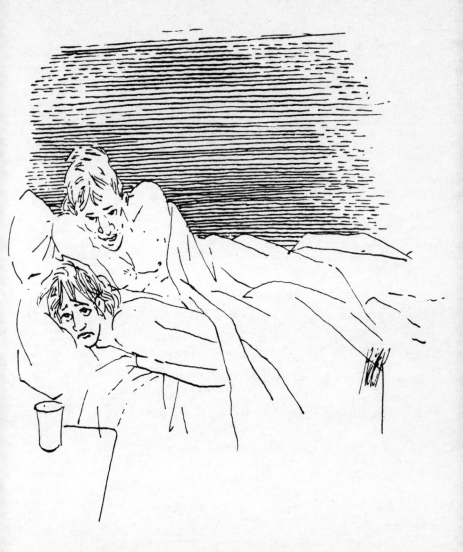

"WASN'T THAT FANTASTIC!"

"WELL, HAVE WE TRIED EVERYTHING?"

" MY WIFE THINKS
I'M IMPOTENT "

" KEEP ON LIKE THAT DUCKS
AND YOU'LL DO FINE "

"COME TO THAT, DEREK, IT HASN'T MEANT MUCH TO ME FOR **YEARS**."

"OH COME ON, GLEN...WHAT'S HAPPENED TO YOUR SENSE OF HUMOUR?"

"NOW WHY DIDN'T WE THINK OF THAT BEFORE? IT COULD BE YOUR FAULT!"

"BYE .... CHAMPION"

"OH LOVE...BUT YOU'RE VERY GOOD AT OTHER THINGS"

"YOU KNOW WHAT THE TROUBLE WITH YOU MEN IS? YOU ALWAYS HAVE TO LEAVE STRAIGHT AFTER".

"IT DOESN'T MATTER
IT'LL BE BETTER NEXT TIME."

"COME ON, LET'S DO IT AGAIN."

"HOW WAS IT FOR YOU?"